THE BIG BOOK OF
SOUL

CW00406894

THE BIG BOOK OF SOUL

This publication is not authorised
for sale in the United States of America
and/or Canada.

Hal Leonard Europe
Distributed by Music Sales

Exclusive Distributors:
Music Sales Limited
8/9 Frith Street, London W1D 3JB, England.

Order No. HLE90001146
ISBN 0-7119-8692-4

Unauthorised reproduction of any part of this
publication by any means including photocopying
is an infringement of copyright.

Cover design by Paula Snell
Cover photographs courtesy of
Harry Goodwin/Redferns (Aretha Franklin) &
Michael Ochs Archive/Redferns (James Brown)
Printed in the USA

Your Guarantee of Quality
As publishers, we strive to produce every book to
the highest commercial standards.The book has
been carefully designed to minimise awkward page
turns and to make playing from it a real pleasure.
Throughout, the printing and binding have been
planned to ensure a sturdy, attractive publication
which should give years of enjoyment. If your copy
fails to meet our high standards, please inform us
and we will gladly replace it.

www.musicsales.com

AMEN

By OTIS REDDING

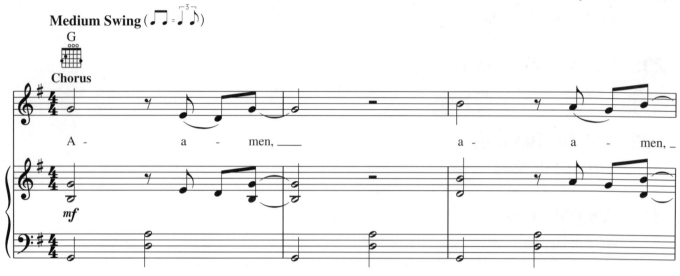

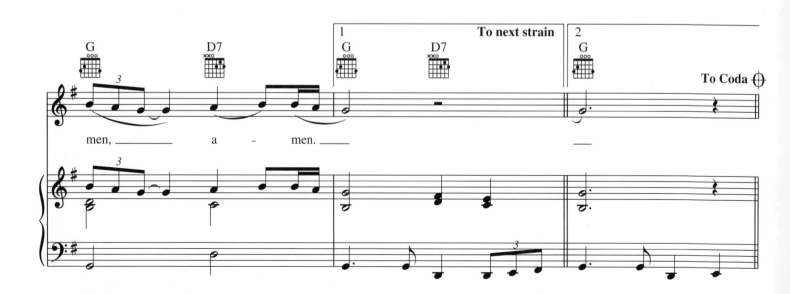

Copyright © 1968 IRVING MUSIC, INC.
Copyright Renewed
All Rights Reserved   Used by Permission

shine, _____ to show my love. _____ 2. One thing my pap - py used to say. He say that

And then I said, "Dad - dy help me sing this line one time: _____

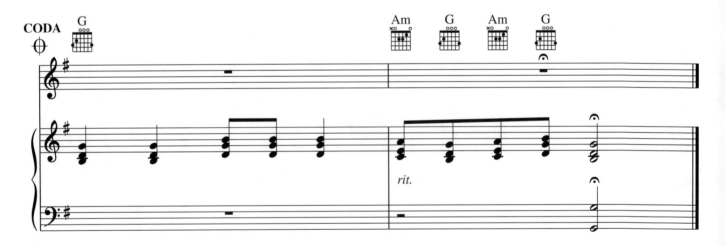

rit.

Additional Lyrics

2. One thing my pappy used to say. He say that
   "Even in my home, son, (I said, 'What, dad?')
   I'm gonna let it shine. (He said:)
   Even in your home, son,
   You've got to let your little light shine.

   Even in your home, son,
   You've got to let it shine.
   Just let it shine, just let it shine,
   To show your love."
   And then I said, "Daddy, help me sing this line one time."
   To Chorus

CHAINS OF LOVE

Words and Music by A. NUGETRE
and HARRY VANWALLS

Copyright © 1956 by Unichappell Music Inc.
Copyright Renewed
International Copyright Secured   All Rights Reserved

Well, it's three o'-clock in the morn-in'; the moon is shin - in'
bright. _____ Yes, it's three o'-clock in the morn-in';
the moon is shin - in' bright. _____ I just sit and won-der
where can you be to - night? _____

BORN UNDER A BAD SIGN

Words and Music by BOOKER T. JONES
and WILLIAM BELL

When I was just a little boy, my daddy left home. He left me and my mama to go it all alone. You know, the times were hard, but somehow we survived. Lord knows, it's a mystery to me how she managed to keep us alive.

Copyright © 1967 IRVING MUSIC, INC.
Copyright Renewed
All Rights Reserved Used by Permission

DO THE FUNKY CHICKEN

Words and Music by
RUFUS THOMAS

Moderately fast

Copyright © 1969 ALMO MUSIC CORP.
Copyright Renewed
All Rights Reserved   Used by Permission

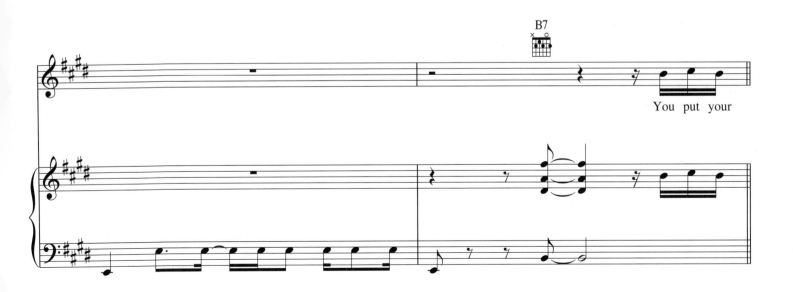

You put your

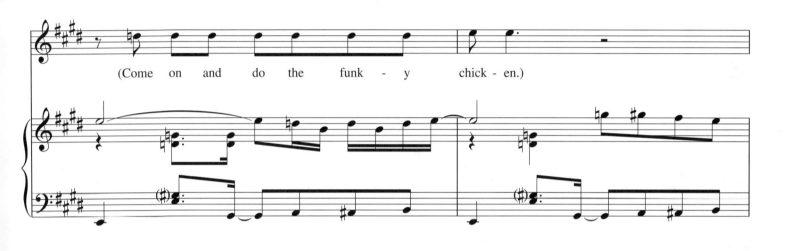

(Come on and do the funk - y chick - en.)

To Coda ⊕

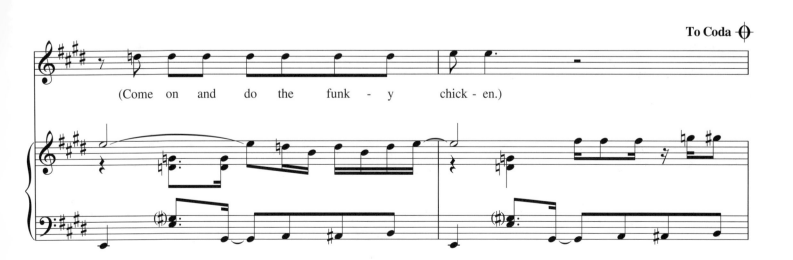

(Come on and do the funk - y chick - en.)

fel - las,   y'all read - y   fel - las,   y'all read - y

fel - las,   y'all read - y   fel - las?

Do __

the funk-y chick-en now.   Do ___ the funk-y chick-en now.

Do   the   funk - y   chick - en   now   all o - ver the place. ___

N.C.

Play 4 times

DO YOUR THING

Words and Music by
ISAAC HAYES

If the

mu - sic makes you move,   'cause you can dig the groove,   then groove

feel like you wan - na scream,   'cause that's your way of let - tin' off steam,   scream

Copyright © 1971 IRVING MUSIC, INC.
Copyright Renewed
All Rights Reserved Used by Permission

29

EVERYDAY PEOPLE

Words and Music by
SYLVESTER STEWART

© 1969 MIJAC MUSIC
All Rights Administered by WARNER-TAMERLANE PUBLISHING CORP.
All Rights Reserved   Used by Permission

GEE WHIZ

Words and Music by
CARLA THOMAS

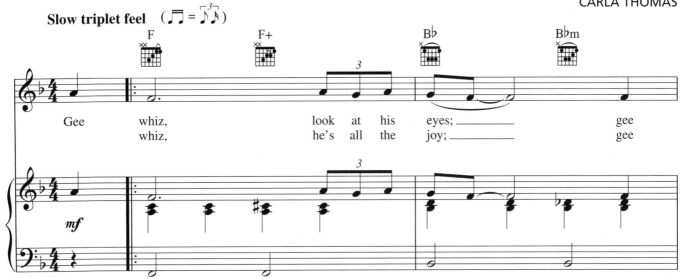

Gee whiz, look at his eyes; _____ gee
whiz, he's all the joy; _____ gee

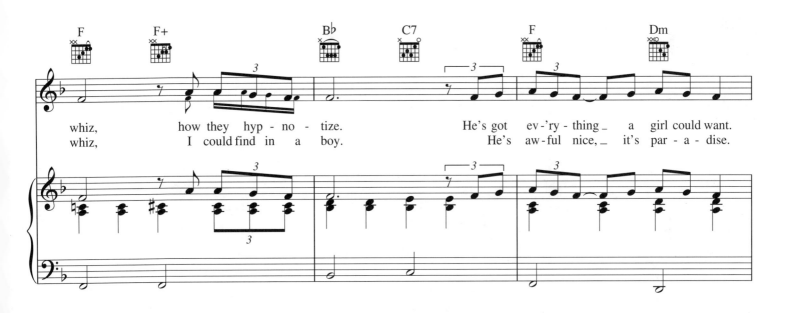

whiz, how they hyp-no-tize. He's got ev-'ry-thing_ a girl could want.
whiz, I could find in a boy. He's aw-ful nice,_ it's par-a-dise.

Man, oh man, what a prize! _____ Gee
I hope I'm not his, be-

Copyright © 1960 IRVING MUSIC, INC.
Copyright Renewed
All Rights Reserved   Used by Permission

GREEN ONIONS

Written by AL JACKSON, JR., LEWIS STEINBERG,
BOOKER T. JONES and STEVE CROPPER

© 1962 (Renewed 1990) AL JACKSON JR. MUSIC (BMI)/Administered by BUG MUSIC and IRVING MUSIC, INC.
All Rights Reserved   Used by Permission

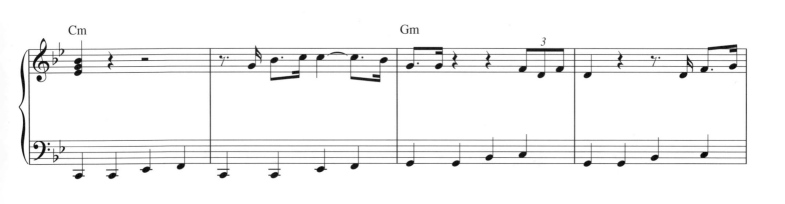

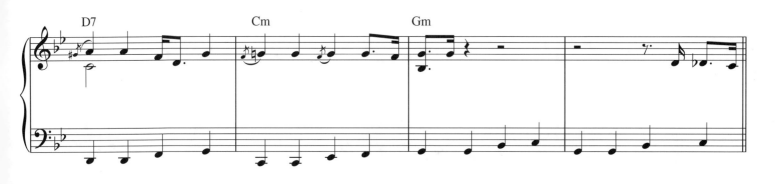

HALLELUJAH I LOVE HIM (HER) SO

Words and Music by
RAY CHARLES

Copyright © 1956 by Unichappell Music Inc.
Copyright Renewed
International Copyright Secured   All Rights Reserved

THE HAPPY SONG

Words and Music by OTIS REDDING
and STEVE CROPPER

Moderately

1. We're sing'n' this song, y'all, sing-in' it for my
2., 3. *(See additional lyrics)*

ba - by. She's the on - ly one can bring me joy;

that's why I sing these hap-py songs. They go: Dum - dum, di - di - di, dum - dum,

Chorus:

Copyright © 1968 IRVING MUSIC, INC.
Copyright Renewed
All Rights Reserved   Used by Permission

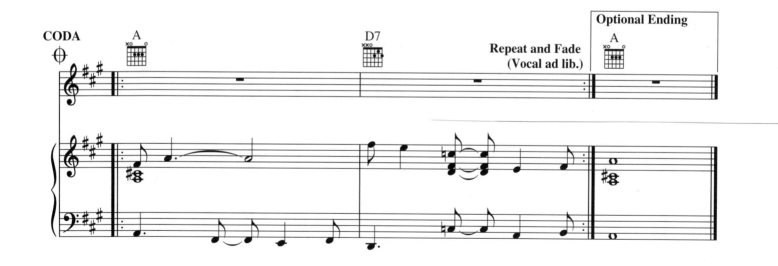

Additional Lyrics

2. On a cold, windy, rainy night,
She shut all my doors, she cut off the light.
She hold me and squeeze me tight,
She tell me: "Big O, everything's all right," and I go
To Chorus

3. Bring my breakfast to the table;
When I go to work she know I'm able.
Do my job, when I come back in,
You oughta' see my baby's face, she just grin, grin, grin.
To Chorus

HARD TO HANDLE

Words and Music by ALLEN JONES,
ALVERTIS BELL and OTIS REDDING

Moderate Funk

1.,3. Ba - by, here I am ___ I'm a man on the scene. ___
2. *(See additional lyrics)*

I can give you what you want, ___ but you got to go home ___ with me.

I've got some good ___ old lov - in' and I've got some in store. ___

Copyright © 1968 IRVING MUSIC, INC.
Copyright Renewed
All Rights Reserved   Used by Permission

When I get __ through throw - in' it on __ you, you got to come back for more. __

Boys and things will come __ by the doz - en; but that ain't noth - in' but drug - store lov - in'.

Pret - ty lit - tle thing, let me light the can - dle, 'cause ma - ma I'm sure __ hard to han - dle now, yes I am.

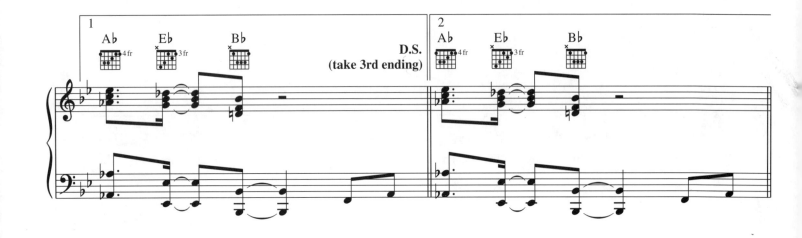

Additional Lyrics

2. Action speaks louder than words, and I'm a man with a great experience.
   I know you got you another man, but I can love you better than him.
   Take my hand, don't be afraid, I want to prove every word that I said.
   I'm advertising love for free, so won't you place your ad with me?
   Boys will come a dime by the dozen, but that ain't nothin' but kiss and look.
   Pretty little thing, let me light the candle, 'cause mama, I'm sure hard to handle, now.

I CAN'T STOP LOVING YOU

Words and Music by
DON GIBSON

Copyright © 1958 Sony/ATV Songs LLC
Copyright Renewed
All Rights Administered by Sony/ATV Music Publishing, 8 Music Square West, Nashville, TN 37203
International Copyright Secured   All Rights Reserved

HOLD ON I'M COMIN'

Words and Music by ISAAC HAYES
and DAVID PORTER

Copyright © 1966 IRVING MUSIC, INC. and PRONTO MUSIC
Copyright Renewed
All Rights Reserved   Used by Permission

I GOT YOU
(I Feel Good)

Words and Music by
JAMES BROWN

Woh!   I feel   good. _____

I knew that I would _____ now.
Ah, sug - ar and spice. _____

I feel _____ good.
I feel _____ nice.

Copyright © 1966 by Fort Knox Music Inc.
Copyright Renewed
International Copyright Secured   All Rights Reserved
Used by Permission

60

I THANK YOU

Words and Music by ISAAC HAYES
and DAVID PORTER

Copyright © 1968 ALMO MUSIC CORP. and WALDEN MUSIC, INC.
Copyright Renewed
All Rights Reserved   Used by Permission

I'LL BE YOUR SHELTER
(In Time of Storm)

Words and Music by CARL HAMPTON,
HOMER BANKS and RAYMOND JACKSON

Copyright © 1971 IRVING MUSIC, INC. and KLONDIKE MUSIC
Copyright Renewed
All Rights Controlled and Administered by IRVING MUSIC, INC.
All Rights Reserved   Used by Permission

I'VE BEEN LOVING YOU TOO LONG

Words and Music by OTIS REDDING
and JERRY BUTLER

Slowly

1. I've been lov-ing you _____
2. (See additional lyrics)

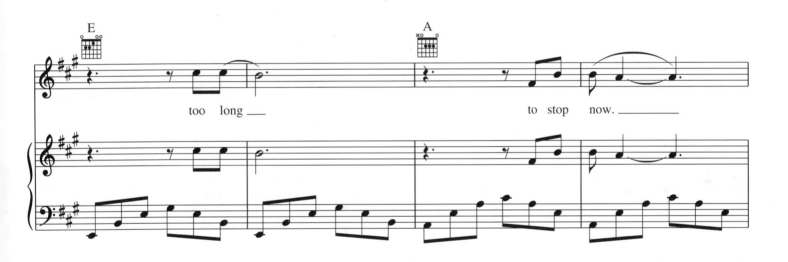

too long ___ to stop now. ___

You are tired _____ and you

Copyright © 1965 IRVING MUSIC, INC.
Copyright Renewed
All Rights Reserved   Used by Permission

Additional Lyrics

2. With you, my life has been so wonderful;
   I can't stop now.
   You are tired,
   And your love is growing cold;
   My love is growing stronger,
   As our affair grows old.
   I've been loving you, a little too long;
   I don't wanna stop now.

I'LL COME RUNNING BACK TO YOU

Words and Music by
WILLIAM COOK

Folks say that you ___ found ___ some - one new to do the things ___ I used to do for you. Just call my name; I'm ___ not a - shamed.

Copyright © 1951 Sony/ATV Songs LLC
Copyright Renewed
All Rights Administered by Sony/ATV Music Publishing, 8 Music Square West, Nashivlle, TN 37203
International Copyright Secured   All Rights Reserved

I'LL PLAY THE BLUES FOR YOU

Words and Music by
JERRY BEACH

Copyright © 1971 IRVING MUSIC, INC. and ROGAN PUBLISHING CO.
Copyright Renewed
All Rights Controlled and Administered by IRVING MUSIC, INC.
All Rights Reserved   Used by Permission

I'LL TAKE YOU THERE

Words and Music by
ALVERTIS ISBELL

Copyright © 1972 IRVING MUSIC, INC.
Copyright Renewed
All Rights Reserved   Used by Permission

Come on now. Play on it, play on it.

Ba - by, lit - tle ba - by,

I'M STILL IN LOVE WITH YOU

Words and Music by AL GREEN,
WILLIE MITCHELL and AL JACKSON, JR.

Copyright © 1972 IRVING MUSIC, INC., AL GREEN MUSIC and AL JACKSON JR. MUSIC (BMI)/Administered by BUG MUSIC
Copyright Renewed
All Rights Reserved   Used by Permission

IF LOVING YOU IS WRONG
I DON'T WANT TO BE RIGHT

Words and Music by HOMER BANKS,
CARL HAMPTON and RAYMOND JACKSON

If lov-in' you is wrong, I don't want to be right. If
Am I wrong to fall so deep-ly in love with you,

be-ing right _ means be-ing with-out _ you, I'd rath-er live a wrong-do-ing life. Your
know-ing I got a wife and two lit-tle chil-dren de-pend - ing on me, too? But

Copyright © 1971 IRVING MUSIC, INC.
Copyright Renewed
All Rights Reserved   Used by Permission

IN THE MIDNIGHT HOUR

Words and Music by STEVE CROPPER
and WILSON PICKETT

Copyright © 1965 IRVING MUSIC, INC. and COTILLION MUSIC, INC.
Copyright Renewed
All Rights Reserved   Used by Permission

IF YOU'RE READY
(Come Go With Me)

Words and Music by HOMER BANKS,
CARL HAMPTON and RAYMOND JACKSON

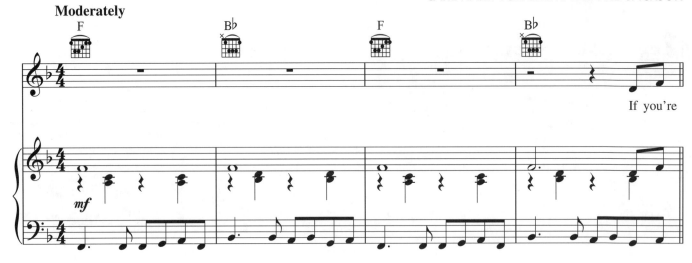

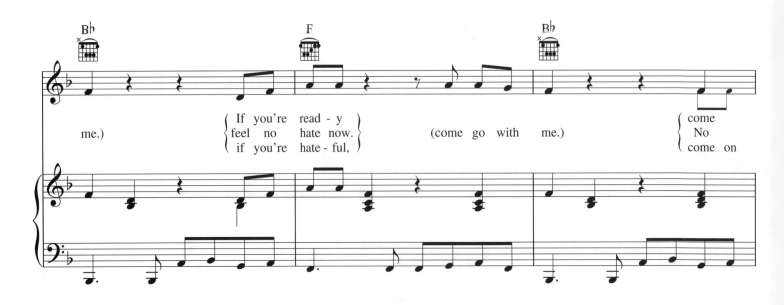

Copyright © 1972 IRVING MUSIC, INC.
Copyright Renewed
All Rights Reserved   Used by Permission

JUST ONE LOOK

Words and Music by DORIS PAYNE
and GREGORY CARROLL

Copyright © 1963 by Careers-BMG Music Publishing, Inc.
Copyright Renewed
International Copyright Secured   All Rights Reserved

KNOCK ON WOOD

Words and Music by EDDIE FLOYD
and STEVE CROPPER

Copyright © 1966 IRVING MUSIC, INC.
Copyright Renewed
All Rights Reserved Used by Permission

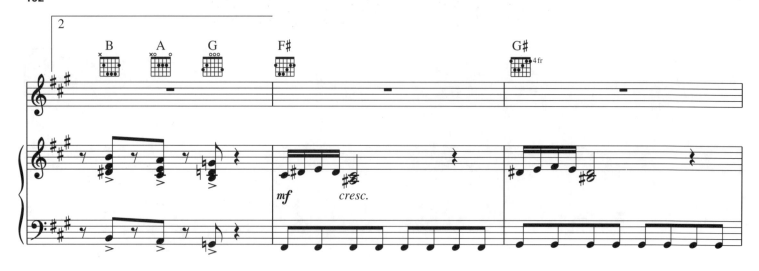

D.S. al Coda

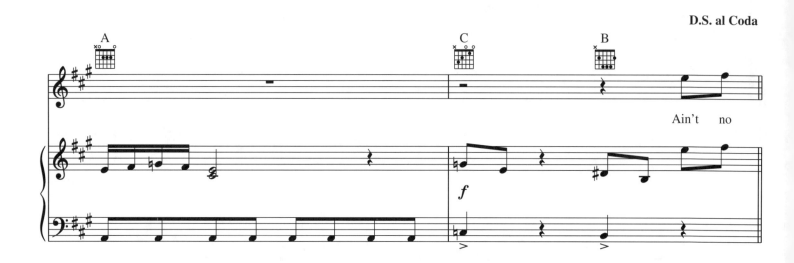

Ain't   no

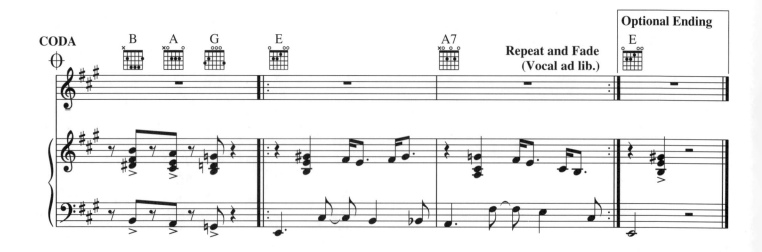

Additional Lyrics

3. Ain't no secret that a woman can feel my love come up.
   You got me seeing, she really sees that, that I get enough.
   Just one touch from you, baby, you know it means so much.
   It's like thunder, lightning;
   The way you love me is frightening,
   I think I better knock-knock-knock-knock on wood.

PAIN IN MY HEART

Words and Music by
NAOMI NEVILLE

Moderate Blues Ballad

Pain in my heart, it's treat-in' me cold.

Where can my ba-by be? Lord, no one know.

Pain in my heart, just won't let me sleep.

Copyright © 1964 (Renewed) by Arc Music Corporation (BMI)
International Copyright Secured   All Rights Reserved
Used By Permission

LAND OF A THOUSAND DANCES

Words and Music by
CHRIS KENNER

© 1963, 1970 (Renewed 1991) EMI LONGITUDE MUSIC
All Rights Reserved   International Copyright Secured   Used by Permission

LITTLE RED ROOSTER

Written by
WILLIE DIXON

© 1961 (Renewed 1989) HOOCHIE COOCHIE MUSIC (BMI)/Administered by BUG MUSIC
All Rights Reserved   Used by Permission

LONELY TEARDROPS

Words and Music by BERRY GORDY,
GWEN GORDY FUQUA and TYRAN CARLO

Moderato, Not Too Fast, With A Beat

LONE - LY TEAR-DROPS, My pil - low's nev - er dry.

LONE - LY TEAR-DROPS, Come home ___ come ___

home. _____ Just say ___ you will, Say ___ you

© 1957 (Renewed 1985) JOBETE MUSIC CO., INC., OLD BROMPTON ROAD and THIRD ABOVE MUSIC
All Rights in the U.S. for JOBETE MUSIC CO., INC. and OLD BROMPTON ROAD Controlled and Administered by EMI APRIL MUSIC INC.
All Rights Reserved   International Copyright Secured   Used by Permission

MR. PITIFUL

Words and Music by OTIS REDDING
and STEVE CROPPER

Copyright © 1965 IRVING MUSIC, INC.
Copyright Renewed
All Rights Reserved   Used by Permission

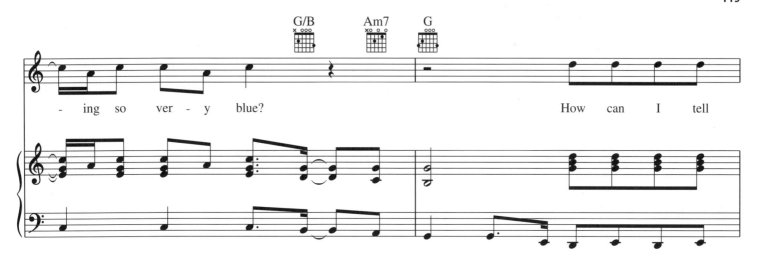

-ing so ver - y blue? How can I tell

you 'bout my fame?__ Oh, _____ don't think t'will do. Yeah, Mis - ter _

D.S. al Coda
(verse 1)

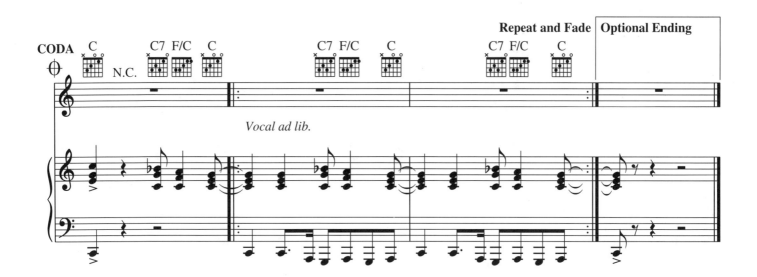

CODA **Repeat and Fade** | **Optional Ending**

Vocal ad lib.

Additional Lyrics

2. They call me Mr. Pitiful; yes, everybody knows, now.
   They call me Mr. Pitiful most every place I go.
   But nobody seems to understand, now, what makes a man sing such a sad song,
   When he lost everything, when he lost everything he had.

PICK UP THE PIECES

Words and Music by JAMES HAMISH STUART,
ALAN GORRIE, ROGER BALL, ROBBIE McINTOSH,
OWEN McINTYRE and MALCOLM DUNCAN

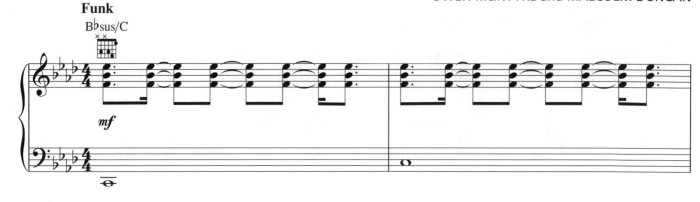

© 1974 AVERAGE MUSIC (ASCAP)/Administered by BUG MUSIC and JOE'S SONGS, INC. (ASCAP)
All Rights Reserved   Used by Permission

pick up   the piec - es.

Bb7sus

Sax solo

RESPECT

Words and Music by
OTIS REDDING

Copyright © 1965 IRVING MUSIC, INC.
Copyright Renewed
All Rights Reserved   Used by Permission

PLEASE ACCEPT MY LOVE

Words and Music by B.B. KING
and SAUL BIHARI

Copyright © 1970 by Careers-BMG Music Publishing, Inc.
Copyright Renewed
International Copyright Secured   All Rights Reserved

RESPECT YOURSELF

Words and Music by MACK RICE
and LUTHER INGRAM

Copyright © 1971 IRVING MUSIC, INC.
Copyright Renewed
All Rights Reserved Used by Permission

A ROSE IS STILL A ROSE

Words and Music by LAURYN HILL,
EDIE BRICKELL, KENNETH WITHROW, JOHN BUSH,
JOHN HOUSER and ALAN ALY

Original Key: G♯ minor. This edition has been transposed down one half-step to be more playable.

Copyright © 1998 Sony/ATV Tunes LLC, Obverse Creation Music, MCA - Geffen Music, Edie Brickell Songs,
Withrow Publishing, Enlightened Kitty and Strange Mind Productions
All Rights on behalf of Sony/ATV Tunes LLC and Obverse Creation Music Administered by
Sony/ATV Music Publishing, 8 Music Square West, Nashville, TN 37203
All Rights on behalf of Edie Brickell Songs, Withrow Publishing, Enlightened Kitty and Strange Mind Productions
Controlled and Administered by MCA - Geffen Music
International Copyright Secured   All Rights Reserved
(contains a sample of "What I Am")

SEE SAW

Words and Music by STEVE CROPPER
and DON COVAY

Some-times you love me

like a good man ought-a;   Some-times you hurt me so

bad _____   my tears run like wa - ter.

Copyright © 1965 IRVING MUSIC, INC. and COTILLION MUSIC
Copyright Renewed
All Rights Reserved   Used by Permission

You get me out _____ right be - fore your

friends, _ then you kiss on me, ba - by, un -

til we're a - lone a - gain. _____ Your love _ is like a

(2nd time, 8va)

see - saw, your love _ is like a see - saw, ba - by.

148

SEND ME SOME LOVIN'

Words and Music by JOHN MARASCALCO
and LEO PRICE

Copyright © 1957 Sony/ATV Songs LLC
Copyright Renewed
All Rights Administered by Sony/ATV Music Publishing, 8 Music Square West, Nashville, TN 37203
International Copyright Secured   All Rights Reserved

THEME FROM SHAFT

Words and Music by
ISAAC HAYES

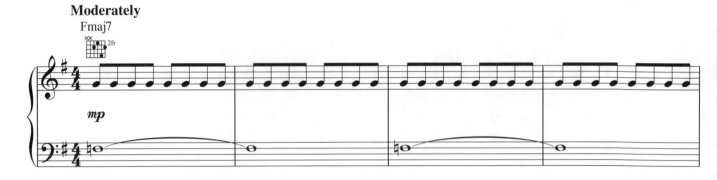

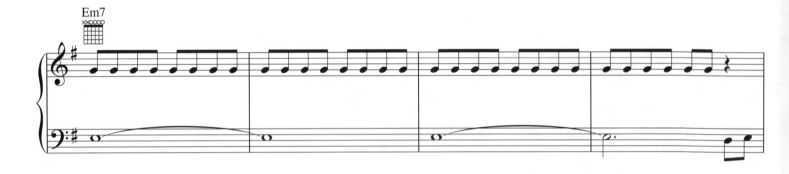

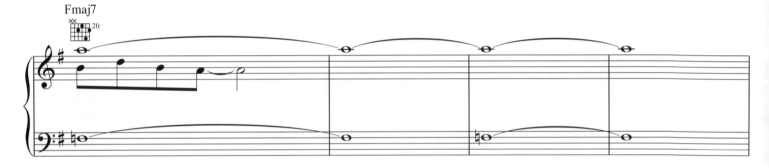

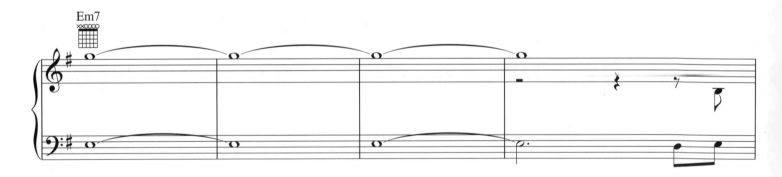

Copyright © 1971 IRVING MUSIC, INC.
Copyright Renewed
All Rights Reserved   Used by Permission

Spoken: Who's the black pri - vate dick ___ that's a sex ma - chine to all the chicks? (Shaft!)

You're damn right!

Sung: Who is the man that would risk his life for his broth - er man? _ (Shaft!)

no one un-der-stands him but his wom-an. (*John   Shaft!*)

(Sittin' On)
THE DOCK OF THE BAY

Words and Music by STEVE CROPPER
and OTIS REDDING

Copyright © 1968, 1975 IRVING MUSIC, INC.
Copyright Renewed
All Rights Reserved   Used by Permission

634-5789

Words and Music by EDDIE FLOYD
and STEVE CROPPER

Copyright © 1966 IRVING MUSIC, INC. and PRONTO MUSIC
Copyright Renewed
All Rights Reserved   Used by Permission

SOUL FINGER

Words and Music by BEN CAULEY,
CARL CUNNINGHAM, JAMES ALEXANDER,
JIMMY KING, PHALON JONES
and RONNIE CALDWELL

Spoken: Soul fin - ger! Soul fin - ger! Soul fin - ger!

Copyright © 1967 IRVING MUSIC, INC.
Copyright Renewed
All Rights Reserved   Used by Permission

Spoken: Soul fin - ger!

Soul fin - ger!

SON OF SHAFT

Words and Music by ALLEN JONES,
HOMER BANKS and WILLIAM BROWN

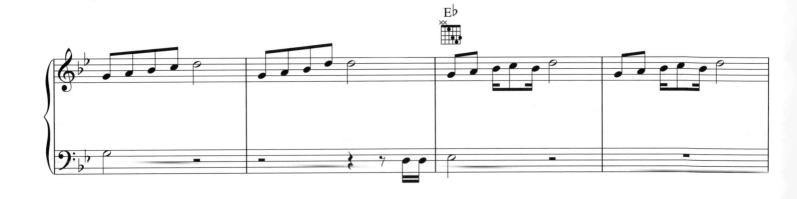

Spoken: Son of Shaft.

Copyright © 1971 IRVING MUSIC, INC.
Copyright Renewed
All Rights Reserved   Used by Permission

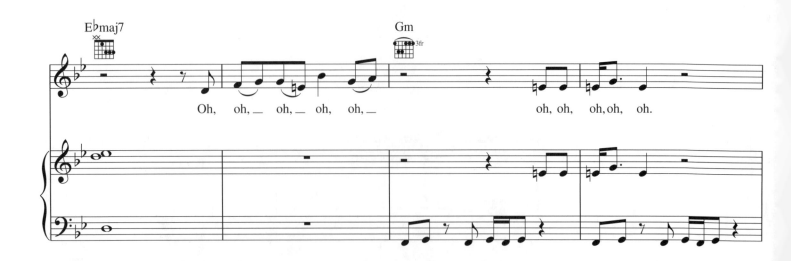

Oh,   oh, __ oh, __ oh,   oh, __   oh, oh,   oh, oh,   oh.

ev - er met the fa - ther, you've _ met the son. _

Yeah, _____

yeah, yeah. _____

Spoken: Check me out.

SOUL LIMBO

Words and Music by BOOKER T. JONES,
DUCK DUNN, STEVE CROPPER
and AL JACKSON, JR.

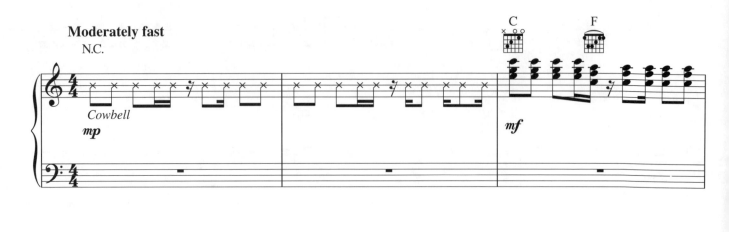

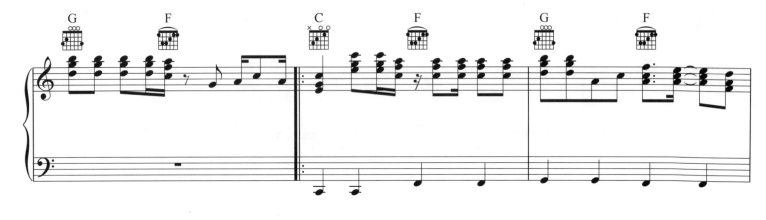

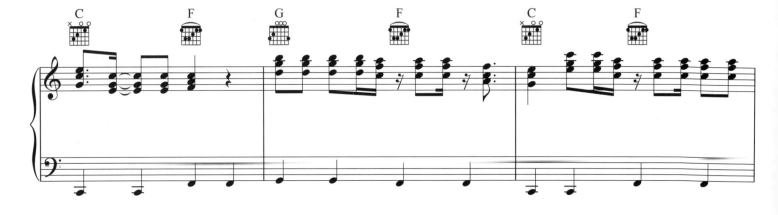

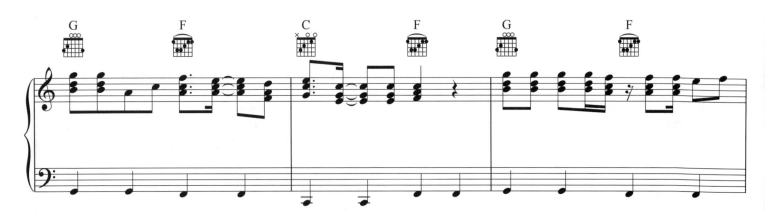

Copyright © 1968 IRVING MUSIC, INC. and AL JACKSON JR. MUSIC (BMI)/Administered by BUG MUSIC
Copyright Renewed
All Rights Reserved   Used by Permission

SOUL MAN

Words and Music by ISAAC HAYES
and DAVID PORTER

Copyright © 1967 ALMO MUSIC CORP. and WALDEN MUSIC, INC.
Copyright Renewed
All Rights Reserved   Used by Permission

STAND BY ME

Words and Music by BEN E. KING,
JERRY LEIBER and MIKE STOLLER

© 1961 (Renewed) JERRY LEIBER MUSIC, MIKE STOLLER MUSIC and MIKE & JERRY MUSIC LLC
All Rights Reserved

TAKE ME TO THE RIVER

Words and Music by AL GREEN
and MABON HODGES

love you like I do, __ af - ter all these chang - es that you put me through. __
treat - ed me so bad. __ Look at all these things __ that we could have had. _____

Copyright © 1974 IRVING MUSIC, INC. and AL GREEN MUSIC, INC.
All Rights Controlled and Administered by IRVING MUSIC, INC.
All Rights Reserved   Used by Permission

TELL IT LIKE IT IS

Words and Music by GEORGE DAVIS
and LEE DIAMOND

Copyright © 1966 (Renewed), 1980 by Olrap Publishing Co., Inc. (BMI) and Conrad Music, a division of Arc Music Corp. (BMI)
International Copyright Secured   All Rights Reserved
Used by Permission

THE THRILL IS GONE

Words and Music by ROY HAWKINS
and RICK DARNELL

The thrill is gone.___ The thrill has gone___ a-
The thrill is gone.___ It's gone a-way___ for

way. The thrill is gone,___ ba-by.
good. The thrill is gone,___ ba-by.

The thrill has gone_____ a-way._____
It's gone a-way_____ for good._____

Copyright © 1951 by Careers-BMG Music Publishing, Inc.
Copyright Renewed
International Copyright Secured   All Rights Reserved

TIME IS TIGHT

Words and Music by BOOKER T. JONES, DUCK DUNN,
STEVE CROPPER and AL JACKSON, JR.

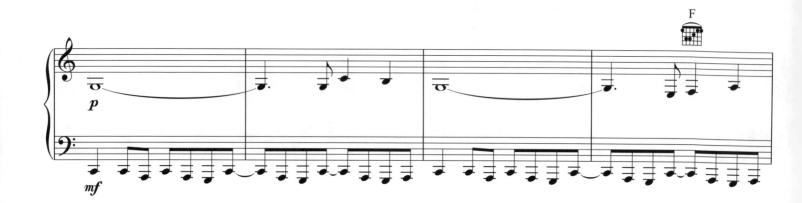

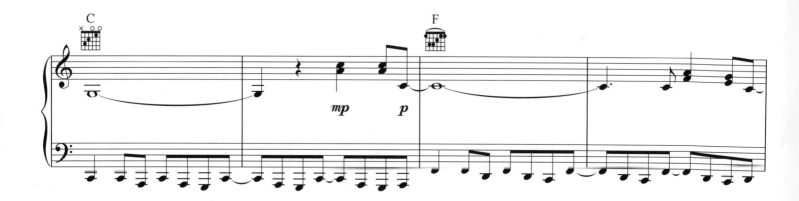

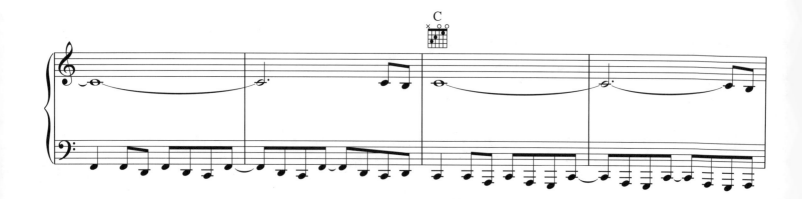

Copyright © 1968 IRVING MUSIC, INC. and AL JACKSON JR. MUSIC (BMI)/Administered by BUG MUSIC
Copyright Renewed
All Rights Reserved   Used by Permission

TIRED OF BEING ALONE

Words and Music by
AL GREEN

Copyright © 1971 IRVING MUSIC, INC. and AL GREEN MUSIC, INC.
Copyright Renewed
All Rights Controlled and Administered by IRVING MUSIC, INC.
All Rights Reserved   Used by Permission

TOUCH A HAND, MAKE A FRIEND

Words and Music by CARL HAMPTON,
HOMER BANKS and RAYMOND JACKSON

Copyright © 1973 IRVING MUSIC, INC.
Copyright Renewed
All Rights Reserved   Used by Permission

UNCHAIN MY HEART

Words and Music by BOBBY SHARP
and TEDDY POWELL

Copyright © 1960 (Renewed) by B. Sharp Music
Print Rights for the U.S. and All Rights for Canada Controlled by Music Sales Corporation (ASCAP)
International Copyright Secured All Rights Reserved
Reprinted by Permission

WALKIN' THE DOG

Words and Music by
RUFUS THOMAS

Copyright © 1963 ALMO MUSIC CORP.
Copyright Renewed
All Rights Reserved   Used by Permission

WHAT'D I SAY

Words and Music by
RAY CHARLES

Copyright © 1959 by Unichappell Music Inc.
Copyright Renewed
International Copyright Secured   All Rights Reserved

WRAP IT UP

Words and Music by ISAAC HAYES
and DAVID PORTER

I've been watch-in' you ___ for days now, ba - by.

Copyright © 1968 IRVING MUSIC INC. and PRONTO MUSIC INC.
Copyright Renewed
All Rights Reserved   Used by Permission

God al-might-y, come on.

Ooh, _____ I'm gon-na treat you

like the queen you are; bring you sweet things _____ from my

can-dy jar, 'cause you've got treats you ain't

wrap it up, _____ I'll take _

_ it. Wrap it up, _____ I'll take _

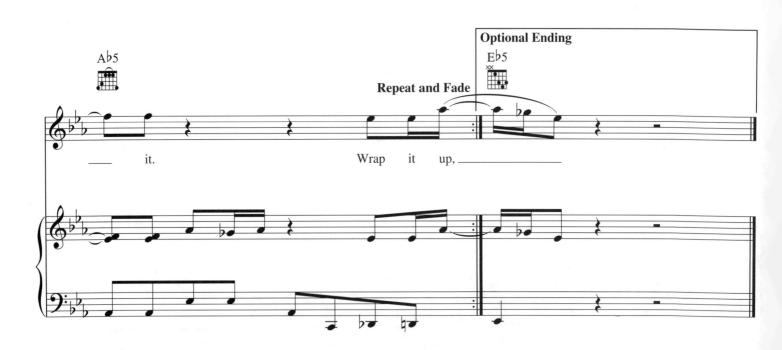

_ it. Wrap it up, _____

YOU DON'T KNOW LIKE I KNOW

Words and Music by ISAAC HAYES
and DAVID PORTER

You don't know_ like I _____ know what that wom-an has done for me._

_____ In the morn-ing she's my wa - ter, in the

Copyright © 1965 IRVING MUSIC, INC. and COTILLION MUSIC, INC.
Copyright Renewed
All Rights Reserved   Used by Permission

YOU DON'T KNOW ME

from CLAMBAKE

Words and Music by CINDY WALKER
and EDDY ARNOLD

Copyright © 1955 by Unichappell Music Inc.
Copyright Renewed
International Copyright Secured All Rights Reserved